NATIONAL GEOGRAPHIC
Reach
for Reading
COMMON CORE PROGRAM

 NATIONAL GEOGRAPHIC LEARNING |  CENGAGE Learning

Acknowledgments

Grateful acknowledgment is given to the authors, artists, photographers, museums, publishers, and agents for permission to reprint copyrighted material. Every effort has been made to secure the appropriate permission. If any omissions have been made or if corrections are required, please contact the Publisher.

Cover Design and Art Direction: Visual Asylum

Cover illustration: Joel Sotelo

Illustration Credits: All illustrations by National Geographic Learning

Photographic Credits: PM2.2 (all) John Paul Endress; **PM2.6** (all) Clem Spalding; **PM2.22** (all) Clem Spalding; **PM4.2a–PM4.2b** Clem Spalding; **PM5.13** (tl, cl, cr, bl) Photodisc/Getty Images, (tc) Peter Sherrard/Getty Images, (tr) Clem Spalding,; **PM5.13a** (tl) Clem Spalding, (tr, cr, bl, bg,) Photodisc/Getty Images, (br) Marian Bacon/Animals Animals; **PM5.23** (tl) Chase Swift/Corbis, (tr) Jeff Rotman/Getty Images, (cl, c) Photodisc/Getty Images, (bl) Stuart Westmoreland/Getty Images; **PM5.23b** (tl) Pat Hermansen/Getty Images, (tr) Photodisc/Getty Images, (cr, bl, br) Getty Images; **PM6.2a** (tl) Peter Johnson/Corbis, (tr) Clem Spalding, (bl) James L. Amos/Corbis; **PM6.2b** (tl) Darrel Gulin/Corbis, (tl) Erick Hosking/Corbis, (cr, bl) David Spears/Corbis; **PM 6.12** (all) Clem Spalding; **PM6.31a** (tl) Jim Cumins/Getty Images, (tr) Elyse Lewin/Getty Images, (bl, br) Photodisc/Getty Images; **PM6.31b** (tl, tr, cl) Stockbyte, (cr, bl) Clem Spalding, (br) Author Tilley/Getty Images; **PM 7.2a** (tl, tr, cl) Clem Spalding, (bg) Emily Wamsteker/AP Photo, (bl, bc) Getty Images; **PM7.2b** (tl, tr, bl, br) Clem Spalding, (bg) Emily Wamsteker/AP Photo, (cr) Getty Images; **PM7.12a–PM7.12b** Clem Spalding; PM9.3 (tl) Getty Images, (tr) Clem Spalding.

For product information and technology assistance, contact us at
Customer & Sales Support, 888-915-3276

For permission to use material from this text or product, submit all requests online at **www.cengage.com/permissions**
Further permissions questions can be emailed to
permissionrequest@cengage.com

National Geographic Learning | Cengage Learning
1 Lower Ragsdale Drive
Building 1, Suite 200
Monterey, CA 93940

Cengage Learning is a leading provider of customized learning solutions with office locations around the globe, including Singapore, the United Kingdom, Australia, Mexico, Brazil, and Japan. Locate your local office at **www.cengage.com/global**.

Cengage Learning products are represented in Canada by Nelson Education, Ltd.

Visit National Geographic Learning online at **NGL.Cengage.com**
Visit our corporate website a **www.cengage.com**

Printed in the USA.
RR Donnelley, Harrisonburg, VA

ISBN: 978-13054-98952 (Practice Book)

ISBN: 978-13056-58677 (Practice Masters)

Teachers are authorized to reproduce the practice masters in this book in limited quantity and solely for use in their own classrooms.

Printed in the United States of America
15 16 17 18 19 20 21 22 23 24
13 12 11 10 9 8 7 6 5 4 3 2 1

Contents

Unit 1: Step Into School

Unit 2: My Family and Me

Unit 3: Visit the Farm!

Unit 4: All Kinds of Plants

Name _____

Learn the Alphabet

Aa Bb Cc Dd

Ee Ff Gg

Hh Ii Jj Kk

Ll Mm Nn Oo Pp

Qq Rr Ss

Tt Uu Vv

Ww Xx Yy Zz

Directions: Have children cut out each strip and mix up the strips. Then sing the alphabet song and have children put the strips in the correct order.

For use with TE p. T20   **PM1.1**   **Unit 1** | Step Into School

Name _____

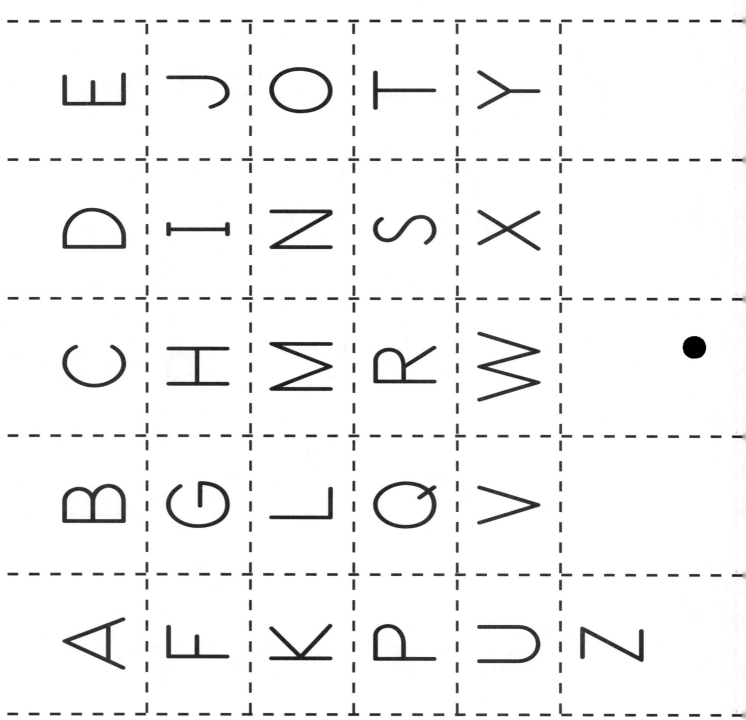

Directions: Have children cut out the letters for use in letter recognition and matching activities. Children can store their letters in resealable plastic bags.

Name _____

Letter Cards

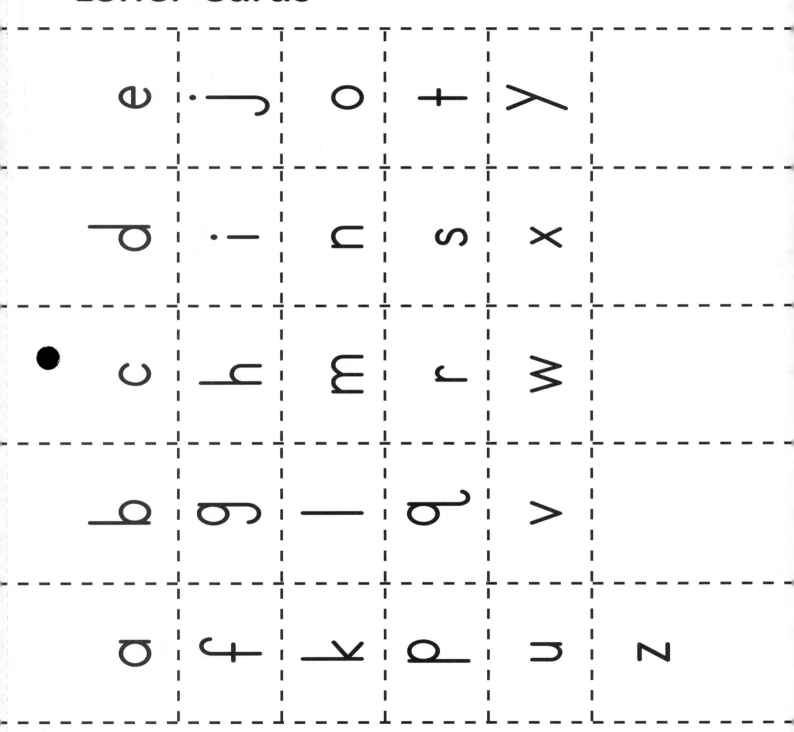

e	j	o	t	y
d	i	n	s	x
c	h	m	r	w
b	g	l	q	v
a	f	k	p	u	z

Directions: Have children cut out the letters for use in letter recognition and matching activities. Children can store their letters in resealable plastic bags.

Name _____

Classroom Rules

1. Raise your hand to talk.

2. Listen carefully to others.

3. Take turns.

4. Share.

Directions: Discuss each rule with children. Have them explain why the rule is important.

Name _____

Classroom Rules

5. Walk. Don't run.

6. Keep your hands to yourself.

7. Clean up.

8. _____

Name _____

Sound for <u>m</u>

Directions: Name each picture. Have children color the pictures whose names begin with the sound for *m*.

Name _____

Sound for <u>m</u>

Directions: Name the letter and each picture with children. Have children cut out the cards. Ask partners to group the pictures whose names begin with the sound for *m*. After they have finished sorting, have partners name all of the pictures in the *Mm* group.

For use with TE p. T52   **PM1.7**   **Unit 1** | Step into School

6

Melon, mmm.

8

More, more. Mmm!

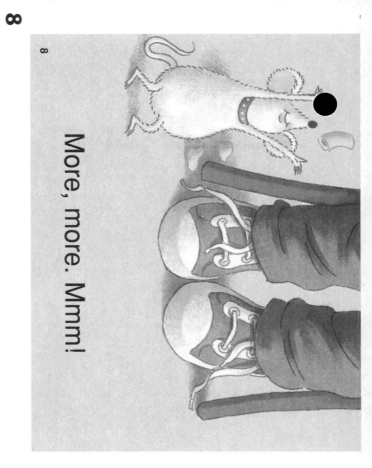

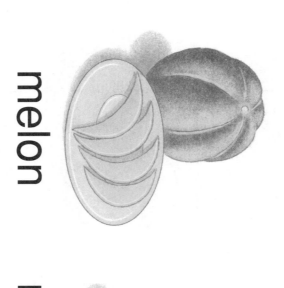

melon   milk

Mm

3

Alphachant™

Mm

by Lada Kratky
illustrated by Mike Reed

HAMPTON-BROWN

8

1

3

Let's Chant!

My mom makes lunch.

Mm

mom   macaroni

Milk, mmm.

Macaroni, mmm.

Phonics and High Frequency Words

Letter and Word Cards

High Frequency
Word

a

●

Mm	Mm	a	a
Mm	Mm	a	a
Mm	Mm	a	a
Mm	Mm	a	a

Directions: Duplicate and cut out letter and word cards. Children will need one of each card for use during practice activities.

My Book of Mm

M m

Directions: Have children trace the letter forms with a finger as you model letter formation. Then have children name and cut out the cards. Have them group the cards that start with the sound for m, and paste one card on each page. Children can write Mm to label their pictures.

© National Geographic Learning, a part of Cengage Learning, Inc.

For use with TE p. T62   **PM1.10**   **Unit 1** | Step into School

Name _____

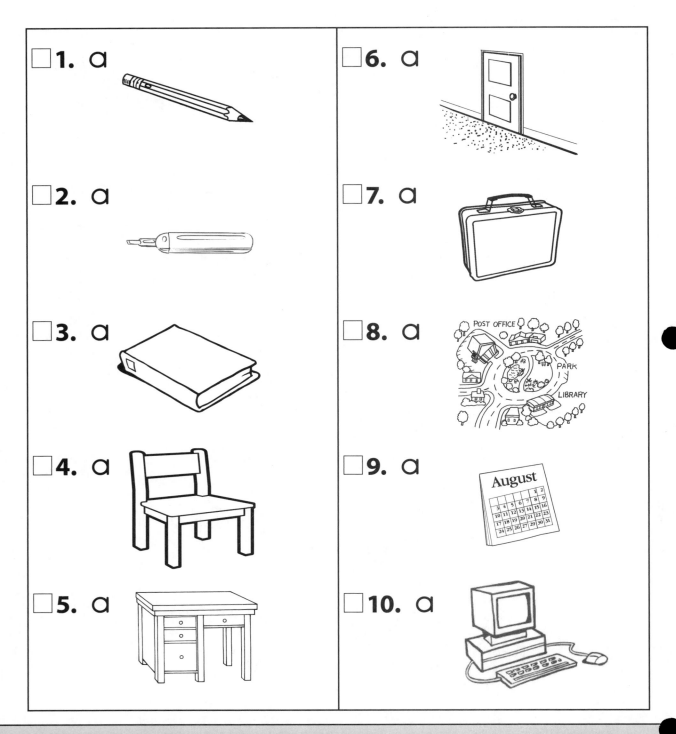

☐ **1.** a

☐ **2.** a

☐ **3.** a

☐ **4.** a

☐ **5.** a

☐ **6.** a

☐ **7.** a

☐ **8.** a

POST OFFICE
PARK
LIBRARY

☐ **9.** a

August

☐ **10.** a

Directions: Name each picture with children. Then have partners take turns reading each label. Ask partners to look for the items on the list in the classroom. Have them check off the items they are able to find.

PM1.11

Unit 1 | Step into School

Comprehension

Sequence Chart

Beginning	Middle	End

Directions: Have children draw one thing that happens at the beginning, in the middle, and at the end of a story they know. Have them tell a partner about their drawings.

© National Geographic Learning, a part of Cengage Learning, Inc.
For use with TE p. T64   **PM1.12**   **Unit 1** | Step into School

Phonics

Sound for m

1.

_____

- - - - - - - - - - -

_____

2.

_____

- - - - - - - - - - -

_____

3.

_____

- - - - - - - - - - -

_____

4.

_____

- - - - - - - - - - -

_____

5.

_____

- - - - - - - - - - -

_____

6.

_____

- - - - - - - - - - -

_____

7.

_____

- - - - - - - - - - -

_____

8.

_____

- - - - - - - - - - -

_____

9.

_____

- - - - - - - - - - -

_____

Directions: Name each picture with children. Have children decide if the word begins with the letter *m*. Ask them to write *m* if the word begins with *m*. Have them leave the line blank if the word doesn't begin with *m*.

For use with TE p. T66   **PM1.13**   **Unit 1** | Step into School

Name _____

Write Labels

1. _____

2. _____

3. _____

4. _____

5. _____

6. _____

Directions: Name each picture with children. Ask what letter all of the picture names begin with. (m) Then have children write the word *a* to complete each label. Ask partners to take turns reading the labels out loud.

© National Geographic Learning, a part of Cengage Learning, Inc.
For use with TE p. T73

Name _____

Sequence Chart

Morning	Noon	Afternoon

Directions: Have children draw something children in the songs do in the morning, at noon, and in the afternoon. Have them tell a partner about their drawings.

For use with TE p. T77   **PM1.15**   **Unit 1** | Step into School

Phonics

Sound for <u>Ss</u>

✂

Ss		
		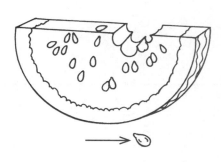
	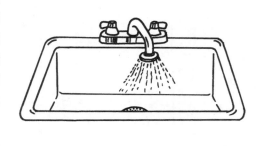	

Directions: Name the letters and each picture with children. Have children cut out the cards. Ask partners to sort by beginning sound. After they have finished sorting, have partners name all of the pictures in the *Ss* group.

My socks are lots of fun!

My socks are in the soap.

by Lada Kratky
photographed by John Paul Endress

HAMPTON-BROWN

Alphachant

Ss

soap

sun

Ss

Ss

socks

sand

Let's Chant!

See my socks!

My socks are in the sun.

My socks are in the sand.

Phonics and High Frequency Words

Letter and Word Cards

S s	S s	a	my
S s	S s	my	my ●
S s	S s	my	my
S s	S s	my	my

Directions: Duplicate and cut out letter and word cards for use during practice activities.

My Book of S s

S s

Directions: Have children trace the letter forms with a finger as you model letter formation. Then have children name and cut out the cards. Have them group the cards that start with the sound for *s* and paste one card on each page. Children can write *Ss* to label their pictures.

© National Geographic Learning, a part of Cengage Learning, Inc.
For use with TE p. T116

PM2.4

Name _____

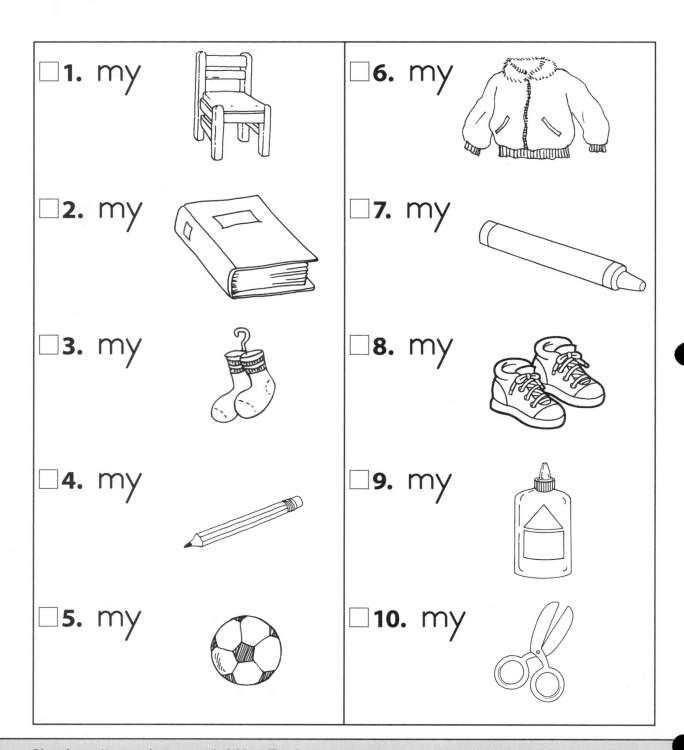

☐ **1.** my

☐ **2.** my

☐ **3.** my

☐ **4.** my

☐ **5.** my

☐ **6.** my

☐ **7.** my

☐ **8.** my

☐ **9.** my

☐ **10.** my

Directions: Name each picture with children. Then have partners take turns reading each label. Ask children to check off items on the list that they have or use at school.

Name _____

Identify Topic and Main Ideas

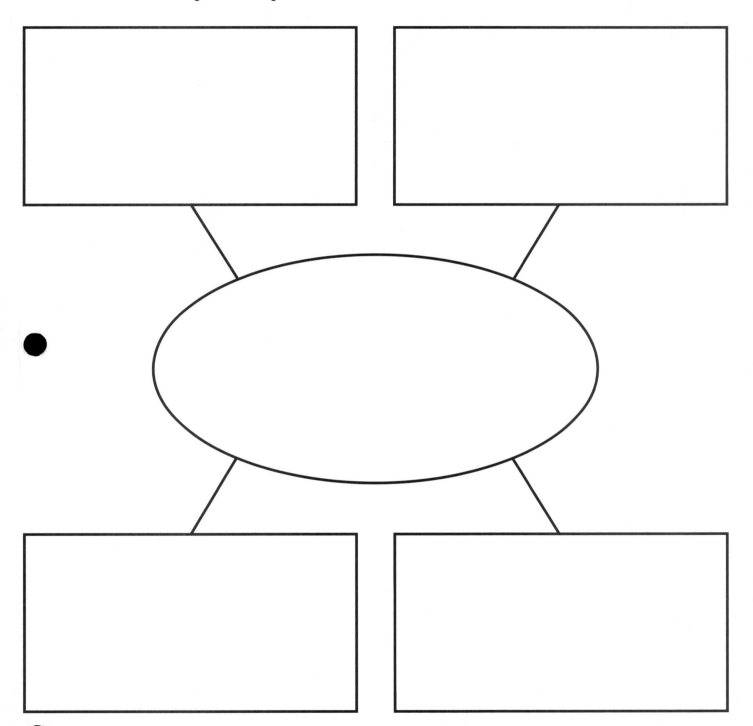

Directions: Have each child draw or write the topic of *Gio and His Family* in the center oval. Then have them draw or write four main ideas from the story in the surrounding boxes.

Phonics

Sound for <u>Ss</u>

1. S	**2.**	**3.**
4.	**5.**	**6.**
7.	**8.**	**9.**

Directions: Name each picture with children. Have children decide if the word begins with the letter s. Ask them to write s if the word begins with s. Have them leave the line blank if the word doesn't begin with s.

For use with TE p. T120 **PM2.7** Unit 2 | My Family and Me

Grammar
Nouns

Directions: Have partners cut out the pictures. Then have them sort the pictures placing people words in one pile, thing words in a second, and place words in a third. Finally, have children take turns choosing two cards from different piles and using the words in an oral sentence.

Phonics and High Frequency Words

Write Labels

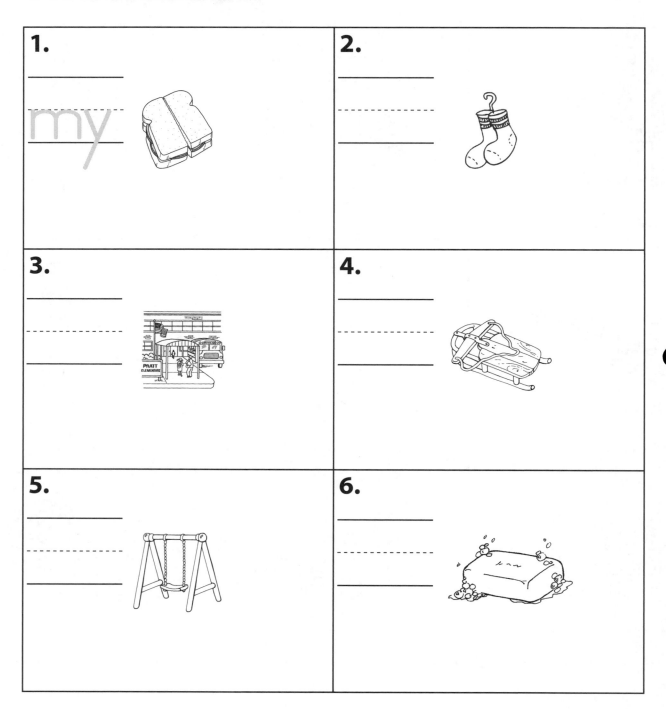

1. _____ ___ ___ ___ ___ my

2. _____ ___ ___ ___ ___

3. _____ ___ ___ ___ ___

4. _____ ___ ___ ___ ___

5. _____ ___ ___ ___ ___

6. _____ ___ ___ ___ ___

Directions: Name each picture with children. Ask what letter all of the picture names begin with. (s) Then have children write the word my or a to complete each label. Ask partners to take turns reading the labels out loud.

Name _____

Compare Texts

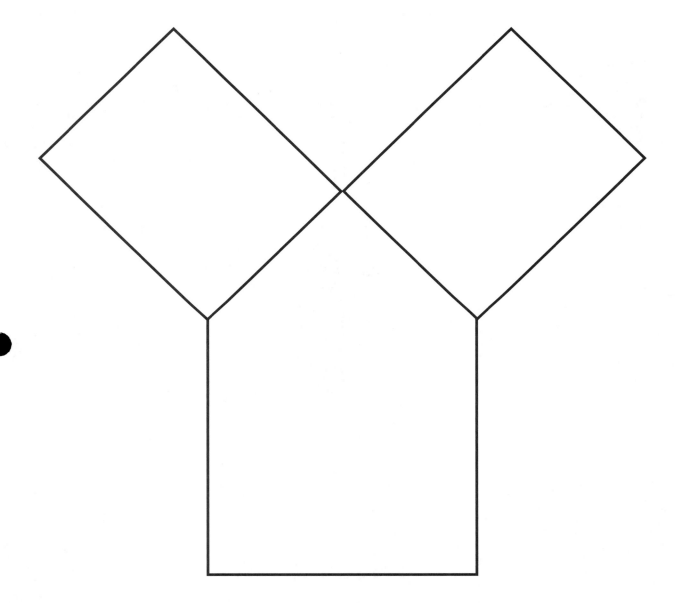

Directions: Have children draw or write about the topic of *Gio and His Family* in the top left box. Have them draw or write about the topic of *A Tasty Treat!* in the top right box. Discuss ways that the two selections are alike. Have children draw one idea in the lower box.

© National Geographic Learning, a part of Cengage Learning, Inc.
For use with TE p. T131   **PM2.10**   **Unit 2** | My Family and Me

Name _____

Sound for T̲t̲

T t	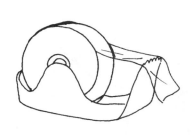	

Directions: Name the letter and each picture with children. Have children cut out the cards. Ask partners to sort by beginning sound, grouping the pictures whose names begin with the sound for *t* with the *Tt* card. Then have partners name all of the pictures in the *Tt* group.

For use with TE p. T146   **PM2.11**   Unit 2 | My Family and Me

tea and toast for Turtle,

Tea and toast for three!

tiger

turtle

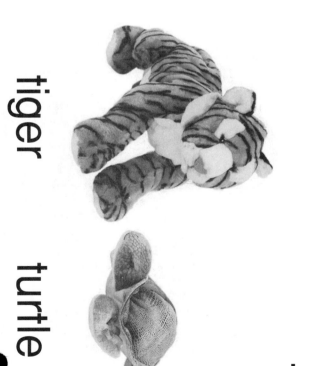

Alphachant

Tt

by Lada Kratky
photographed by Clem Spalding

HAMPTON-BROWN

Tt

T t

table

toast

I'll set the table for tea.

and tea and toast for me.

Tea and toast for Tiger,

Phonics and High-Frequency Words

Letter and Word Cards

Tt	Tt	a	see
Tt	Tt	my	see
Tt	Tt	See	see
Tt	Tt	See	see

Directions: Duplicate and cut out letter and word cards. Children will need one of each card for use during practice activities.

My Book of T t

T t

Directions: Have children trace the letter forms with a finger as you model letter formation. Then have children name and cut out the cards. Have them group the cards that start with the sound for *t*, and paste one card on each page. Children can write *Tt* to label their pictures.

© National Geographic Learning, a part of Cengage Learning, Inc.
For use with TE p. T156   **PM2.14**   Unit 2 | My Family and Me

Name _____

Read Sentences

High Frequency
Word

see

1. See my _____.	**2.** See my _____.
3. See my _____.	**4.** See my _____.

Directions: Have children complete each sentence frame by drawing something they have at home. Have partners share their pictures and read their sentences.

Name _____

Make Predictions

The Snowy Day

Directions: Read the book title aloud. Then have children draw a picture of what they think the book will be about. Prompt them by asking, *What will the story be about?*

Name _____

Sound for T̲t̲

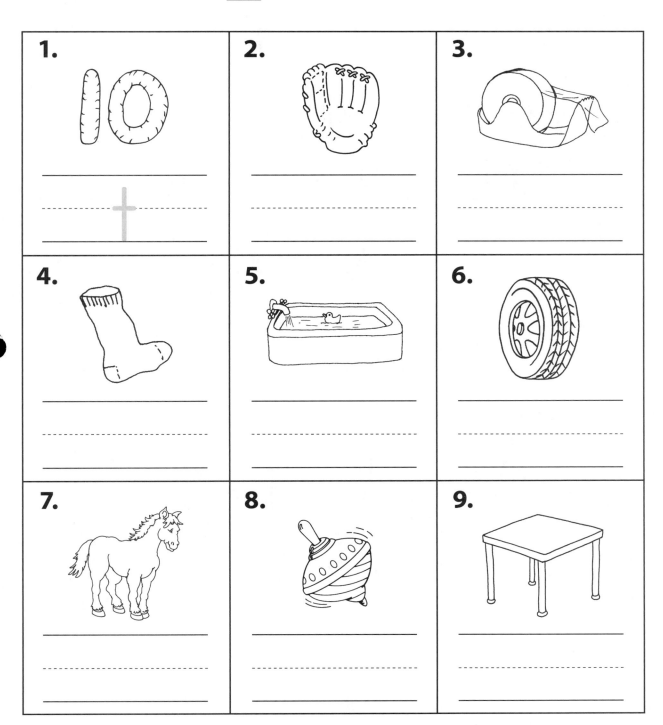

1.

_____

- - - - - - t - - - - - -

2.

_____

- - - - - - - - - - - - -

3.

_____

- - - - - - - - - - - - -

4.

_____

- - - - - - - - - - - - -

5.

_____

- - - - - - - - - - - - -

6.

_____

- - - - - - - - - - - - -

7.

_____

- - - - - - - - - - - - -

8.

_____

- - - - - - - - - - - - -

9.

_____

- - - - - - - - - - - - -

Directions: Name each picture with children. Have children decide if the word begins with the letter *t*. Ask them to write *t* if the word begins with *t*. Have them leave the line blank if the word doesn't begin with *t*.

For use with TE p. T160   **PM2.17**   **Unit 2** | My Family and Me

Grammar

Nouns

Directions: Have children color all the pictures of people green. Have children color all of the pictures of places red. Have children color all of the things blue.

Name _____

Write Sentences

1.

See _____ a top.

2.

_____ a tractor.

3.

_____ a tire.

4.

_____ twins.

5.

_____ a truck.

6.

_____ a turkey.

Directions: Name each picture with children. Ask what letter all of the picture names begin with. (t) Then have children write the word *See* to complete each sentence. Ask partners to take turns reading the sentences out loud.

For use with TE p. T167   **PM2.19**   **Unit 2** | My Family and Me

Name _____

Compare Predictions

Directions: After comparing predictions they made about the week's reading, have children draw and write about one prediction they made. Prompt them by asking, *What did you predict?*

Phonics

Sound for Pp

✂

P p

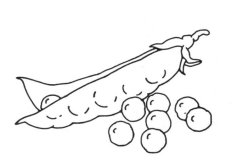

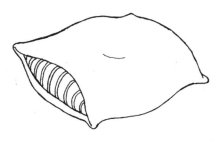

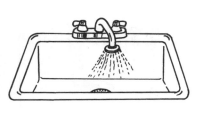

Directions: Name the letter and each picture with children. Have children cut out the cards. Ask partners to sort by beginning sound, grouping the pictures whose names begin with the sound for *p* with the *Pp* card. Have partners name all of the pictures in the *Pp* group.

Unit 2 | My Family and Me

6

Pass the peanuts,

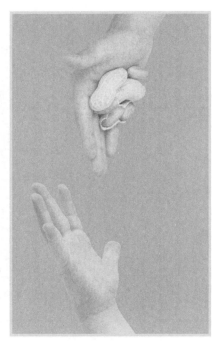

8

Please!

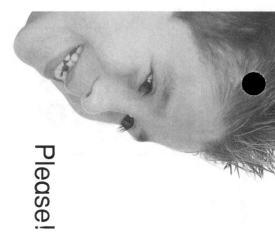

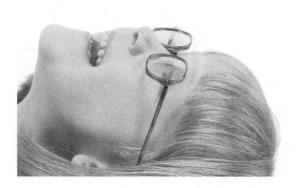

---

peanuts   peas

Pp

3

Alphachant

Pp

by Lada Kratky
photographed by Clem Spalding

HAMPTON-BROWN

1

Pp

pear

peach

Let's Chant!

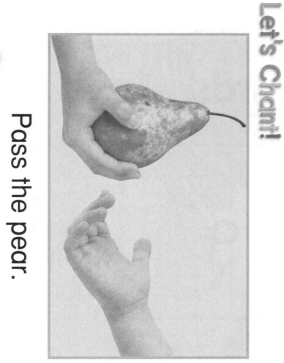

Pass the pear.

and pass the peas.

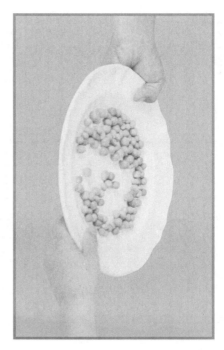

Pass the peach.

Phonics and High-Frequency Words

Letter and Word Cards

Pp	Pp	a	the
Pp	Pp	my	the
Pp	Pp	See	the
Pp	Pp	the	the

Directions: Duplicate and cut out letter and word cards. Children will need one of each card for use during practice activities.

© National Geographic Learning, a part of Cengage Learning, Inc.
For use with TE pp. T188, T189, T197, T200

My Book of P p

P p

Name _____

Read Sentences

1. See the

_____ .

2. See the

_____ .

3. See the

_____ .

4. See the

_____ .

Directions: Have children complete each sentence frame by drawing a food they like. Have partners share their pictures and read their sentences.

© National Geographic Learning, a part of Cengage Learning, Inc.
For use with TE p. T197

PM2.25

Unit 2 | My Family and Me

Name _____

Sequence Chain

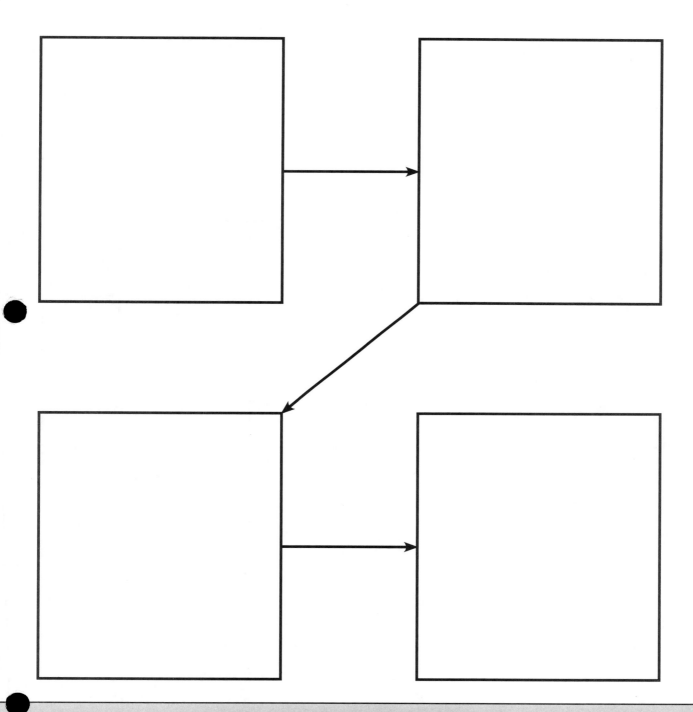

Directions: Have children draw pictures to show the order in which things happen in *Feast for 10*. Point out the arrows that show how to draw the events in the correct order.

© National Geographic Learning, a part of Cengage Learning, Inc.
For use with TE p. T198   **PM2.26**   **Unit 2** | My Family and Me

Name _____

Sound for <u>Pp</u>

1.	**2.**	**3.**
4.	**5.**	**6.**
7.	**8.**	**9.**

Directions: Name each picture with children. Have children decide if the word begins with the letter *p*. Ask them to write *p* if the word begins with *p*. Have them leave the line blank if the word doesn't begin with *p*.

For use with TE p. T200 **PM2.27** **Unit 2** | My Family and Me

Plural Nouns

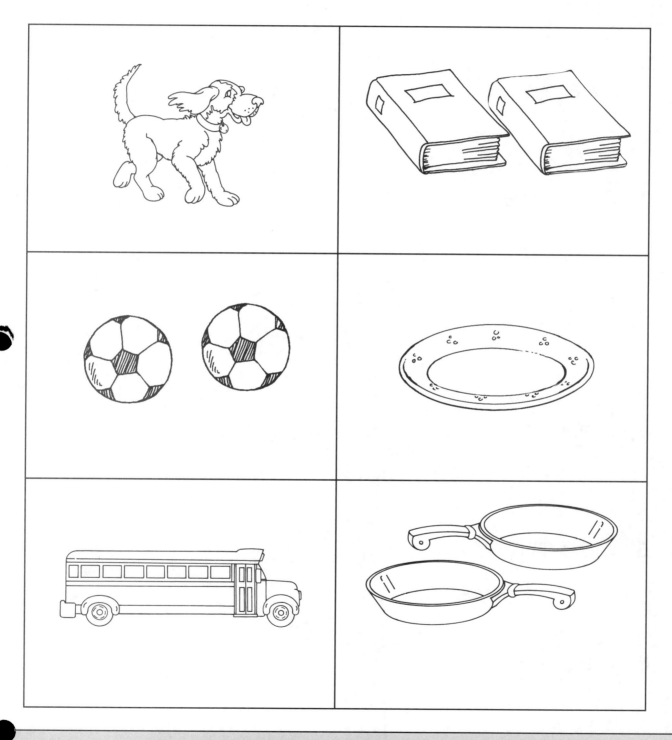

Directions: Have children look at each picture, name it, and tell if it shows one or more than one. Then have them color the pictures that show more than one. When they have finished, have children name the pictures with a partner.

Name _____

Read Sentences

1. See the  .

2. See the  .

3. See a  .

4. See the  .

5. See my  .

6. See the  .

Directions: Name each picture with children. Ask what letter all of the picture names begin with. *(p)* Then have partners take turns reading the sentences out loud.

Name _____

Compare Stories

Directions: After comparing *The Donut* and *Feast for 10,* have children draw and write about one way the stories are alike.

Sound for Cc

 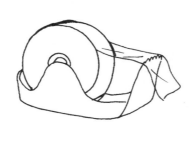 

 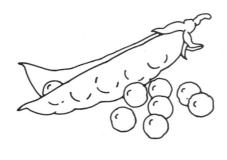 

Directions: Name the letter and each picture with children. Have children cut out the cards. Ask partners to sort by beginning sound, grouping the pictures whose names begin with the sound for *c* with the *Cc* card. Have partners name all of the pictures in the *Cc* group.

© National Geographic Learning, a part of Cengage Learning, Inc.
For use with TE p. T226   **PM2.31**   **Unit 2** | My Family and Me

Camel's car is faster.

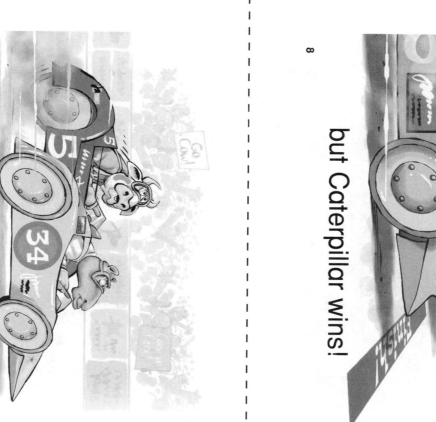

but Caterpillar wins!

Alphachant

Cc

by Lada Kratky
illustrated by Eldon Doty

HAMPTON-BROWN

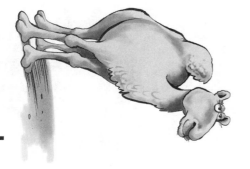

camel

cat

Cc

Cc

car

cow

Cat's car is fastest,

Let's Chant!

There go the cars!

Cow's car is fast.

Phonics and High-Frequency Words

Letter and Word Cards

High Frequency
Word

I

✂

Cc	a	my	I
Cc	Cc	See	I
Cc	Cc	the	I
Cc	Cc	see	I

Directions: Duplicate and cut out letter and word cards. Children will need one of each card for use during practice activities.

For use with TE p. T228, T229, T237, T241   **PM2.33**   **Unit 2** | My Family and Me

My Book of C c

Cc

Directions: Have children trace the letter forms with a finger as you model letter formation. Then have children name and cut out the cards. Have them group the cards that start with the sound for *c* and paste one card on each page. Children can write *Cc* to label their pictures.

© National Geographic Learning, a part of Cengage Learning, Inc.
For use with TE p. T236

PM2.34

Unit 2 | My Family and Me

Read Sentences

1.

___ see a cape.

2.

___ see a carrot.

3.

___ see a camel.

4.

___ see a clam.

5.

___ see a cage.

6.

___ see a cub.

Directions: Name each picture with children. Ask what letter all of the picture names begin with. (c) Then have children write the word I to complete each sentence. Ask partners to take turns reading the sentences out loud.

Name _____

Identify Details

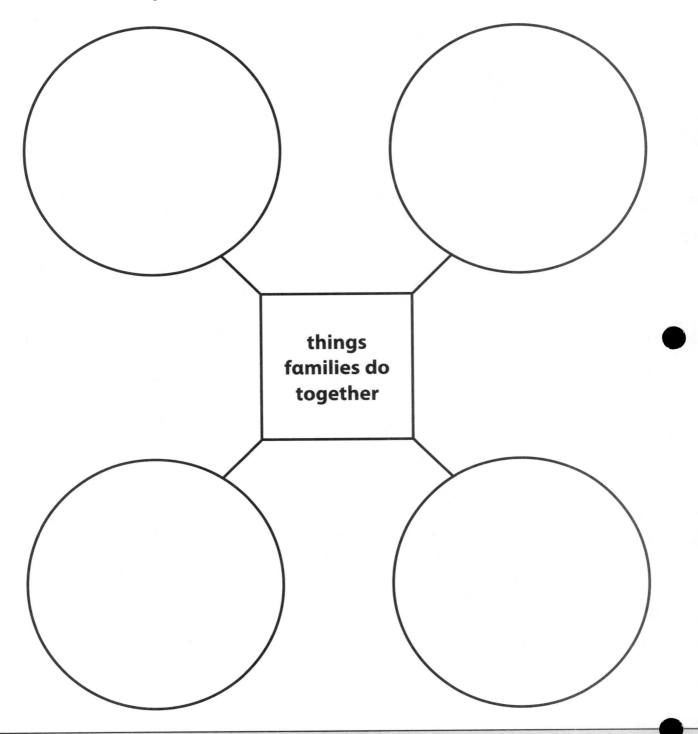

things families do together

Directions: Remind children that the topic of *You and Me Together* is "families." Read the main idea in the center of the idea web. Have each child draw or write one detail from the book in each circle.

© National Geographic Learning, a part of Cengage Learning, Inc.
For use with TE p. T238   **PM2.36**   Unit 2 | My Family and Me

Name _____

1.

2.

3.

4.

5.

6.

7.

8.

9.

Directions: Name each picture with children. Have children decide if the word begins with the sound for the letter *c*. Ask them to write *c* if the word begins with the sound for *c*. Have them leave the line blank if the word doesn't begin with the sound for *c*.

PM2.37

Name _____

Pronouns

Directions: Make enough cards for partners or small groups to each have a set. Cut apart the cards and paste on index cards if necessary. Use the cards as described on TE page T150.

PM2.38

Name _____

Read Sentences

☐ **1.** I see a .

☐ **6.** I see the .

☐ **2.** I see the  .

☐ **7.** I see the .

☐ **3.** I see the .

☐ **8.** I see the .

☐ **4.** I see a .

☐ **9.** I see the .

☐ **5.** I see a .

☐ **10.** I see a .

Directions: Name each picture with children. Then have partners take turns reading each sentence. Ask children to color the pictures whose names begin with the sound for *c*. Then have them check off items that they would like at a birthday party.

Name _____

Compare and Contrast Details

**You and
Me Together**

**Goldilocks and the
Bear Family**

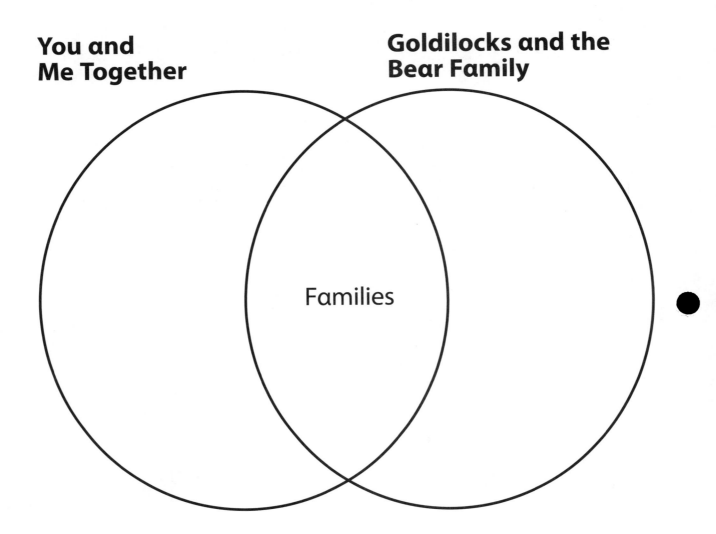

Families

Directions: Read the topic in the center of the Venn diagram. Have children draw or write about a family from *You and Me Together* in the left circle. Have them draw or write about the Bear family in the right circle. Possible responses are shown.

© National Geographic Learning, a part of Cengage Learning, Inc.
For use with TE p. T251   **PM2.40**   **Unit 2** | My Family and Me

Name _____

Sound for <u>a</u>

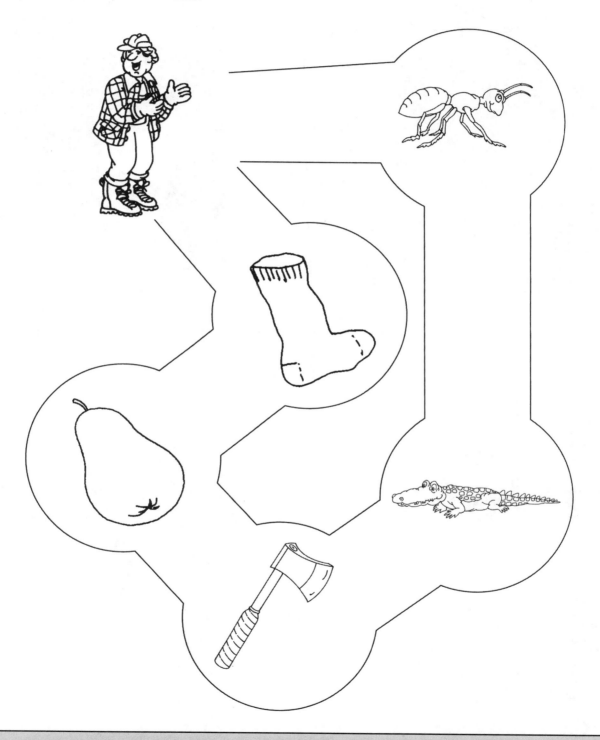

Directions: Tell children the man they see is Adam. Then name the other pictures: *ant, sock, pear, alligator, ax.* Ask children to help Adam find his ax. Have them color each picture along the path whose name begins with /ă/ like astronaut, then draw a line to connect the pictures.

© National Geographic Learning, a part of Cengage Learning, Inc.
For use with TE p. T20   **PM3.1**   **Unit 3** | Visit the Farm!

ants on an apple,

6

Oh, my!

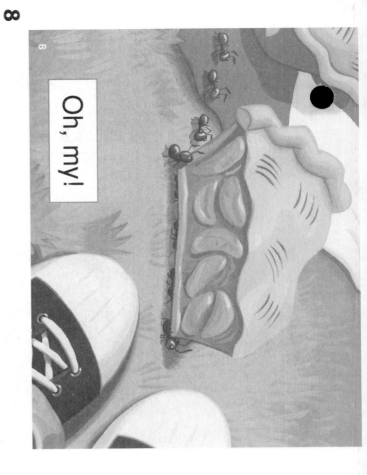

8

Aa

Alphachant™

by Lada Kratky
illustrated by Ken Spengler

HAMPTON-BROWN

1

apple   apple pie

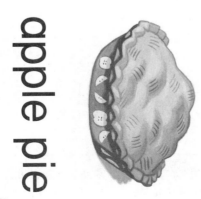

Aa

3

Let's Chant!

Ants, ants, ants!

Aa

ant

anthill

Ants on an anthill,

---

and ants on our apple pie.

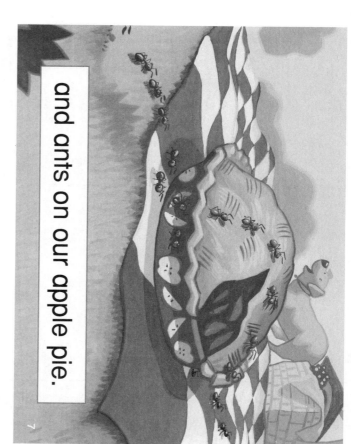

Name _____

High Frequency **Word**
look

●

at

look

am

I

my

see

a

the

Directions: Have children cut out the word cards to use in practice activities. Children can store their words in resealable plastic bags or manila envelopes.

For use with TE p. T22, T23, T31   **PM3.3**   **Unit 3** | Visit the Farm!

My Book of Aa

Aa

Directions: Have children trace the letter forms with a finger as you model letter formation. Then have children name and cut out the cards. Have them group the cards that start with the sound for *a* and paste one card on each page. Children can write *Aa* to label their pictures.

© National Geographic Learning, a part of Cengage Learning, Inc.
For use with TE p. T30   **PM3.4**   **Unit 3** | Visit the Farm!

High Frequency Words

Read Sentences

1. Look! I see a .

2. Look! I see a  .

3. Look! I see a _____ .

Directions: Discuss the pictures. Have partners read the sentences together.

Comprehension

Character Map

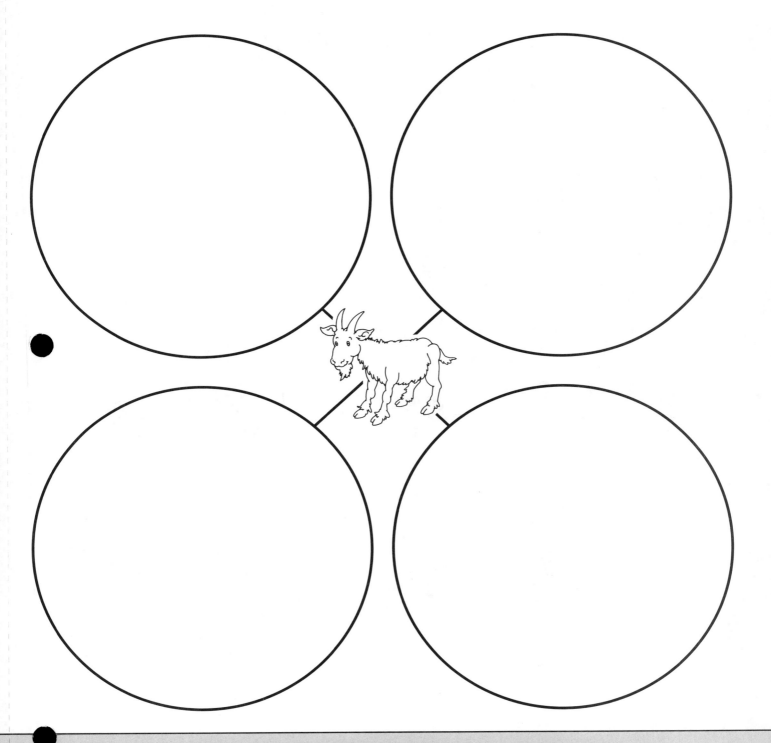

Directions: Fill out a model map together. Then have children draw, dictate, or write to fill in their own maps.

Name _____

Cut-Outs

Directions: Have children color and cut out the characters, and then glue them to craft sticks. Then have children use the puppets to role-play characters from *There's a Billy Goat in the Garden.*

For use with TE p. T33   **PM3.7**   **Unit 3** | Visit the Farm!

Name _____

Blend Words with <u>a</u>

1. cat

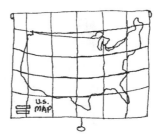

2. map

3. pat

4. cap

5. tap

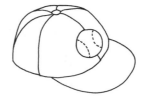

Directions: Have children read each word and draw a line to the picture it matches.

Name _____

Describing Words

1.

big
little

2.

loud
quiet

3.

slow
fast

Directions: Have children color one animal in each box. Then have them circle a word that describes the animal.

For use with TE p. T38   **PM3.9**   **Unit 3** | Visit the Farm!

Name _____

Read Sentences

1. Look at the cat.

2. I pat the cat.

3. Look at the map.

4. I tap the map.

Directions: Discuss the pictures. Have children read the sentences with a partner.

© National Geographic Learning, a part of Cengage Learning, Inc.
For use with TE p. T41   **PM3.10**   **Unit 3** | Visit the Farm!

Name _____

Little Bat and Tiny Bee

tiny bee   Little Bat

Directions: Talk with children about the ways in which tiny bee and Little Bat are alike. Have children choose one idea to write and/or draw in the oval.

For use with TE p. T45   **PM3.11**   **Unit 3** | Visit the Farm!

Phonics

Sound for n̲

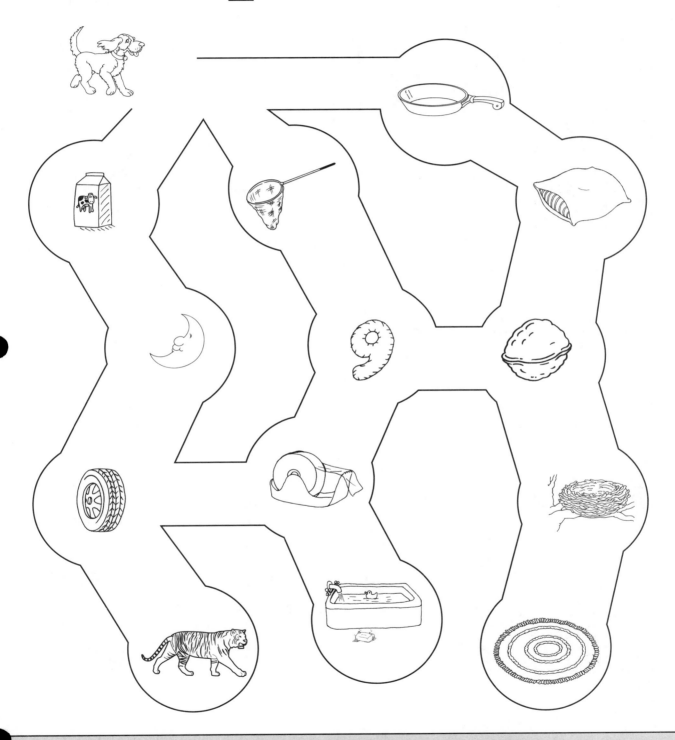

Directions: Tell children that the dog's name is Nipper. Name each picture. Have children color the pictures that start with the sound for n. Then have them draw a line from Nipper to his rug by connecting the colored pictures.

© National Geographic Learning, a part of Cengage Learning, Inc.

For use with TE p. T60   **PM3.12**   **Unit 3** | Visit the Farm!

I see noodles on your toes!

and noodles on your neck.

illustrated by Karen Stormer Brooks
by Lada Kratky

HAMPTON-BROWN

Alphachant

Nn

Nn

nose

neck

Nn

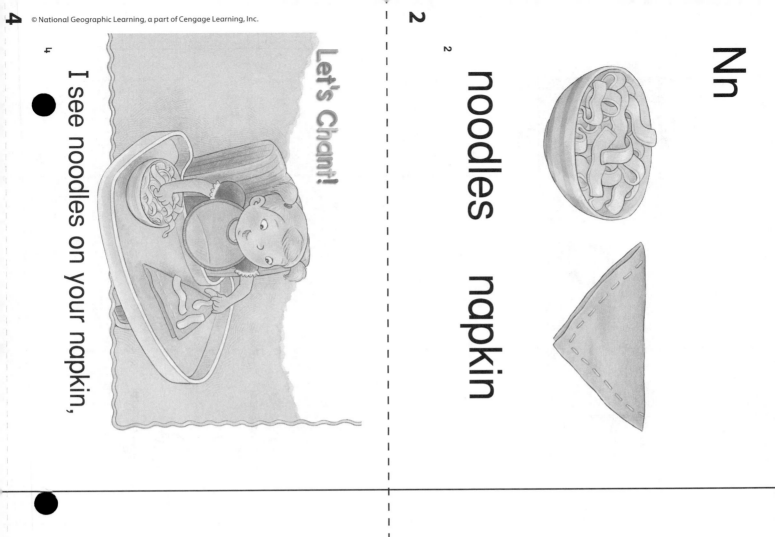

noodles

napkin

Let's Chant!

I see noodles on your napkin,

Oh no, Nelly!

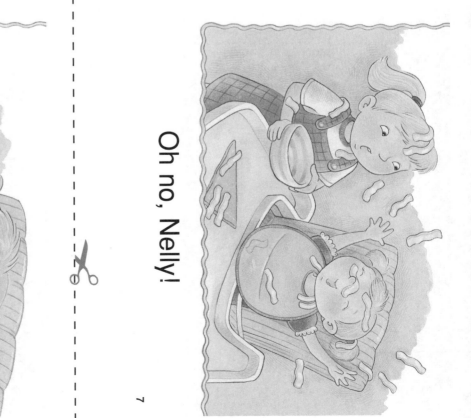

noodles on your nose,

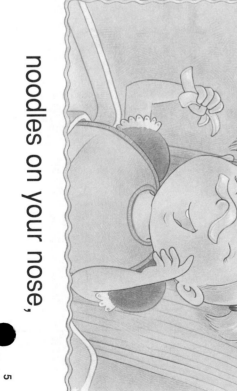

High Frequency Words

Word Cards

| High Frequency |
| **Word** |
| this |

a

I

my

look

see

this

the

My Book of Nn

Nn

Directions: Have children trace the letter forms with a finger as you model letter formation. Then have children name and cut out the cards. Have them group the cards that start with the sound for *n* and paste one card on each page. Children can write *Nn* to label their pictures.

© National Geographic Learning, a part of Cengage Learning, Inc.
For use with TE p. T70

PM3.15

Unit 3 | Visit the Farm!

Name _____

Read Sentences

1. Look at this cat.

2. Look at this cat.

3. I can pat this cat.

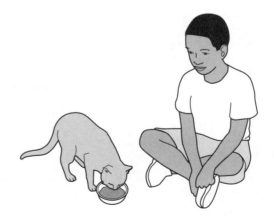

Directions: Discuss the pictures. Have partners read the sentences together.

© National Geographic Learning, a part of Cengage Learning, Inc.
For use with TE p. T71   **PM3.16**   **Unit 3** | Visit the Farm!

Comprehension

Setting

Directions: Have children draw a scene from Honza's Little House. Remind them that they should draw the setting with whatever is in the house at that point. Then have partners share and discuss their drawings.

Blend Words with <u>n</u>

nap
pat

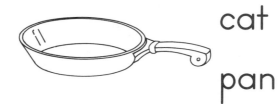
cat
pan

sat
man

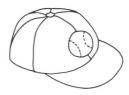
cap
tap

tan
can

cat
nap

Directions: Have children read the words and circle the word that names each picture.

Name _____

Describing Words

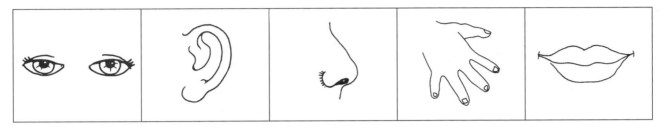

My Favorite Place

Directions: Have each child draw a favorite place. Remind children to include what they see, hear, smell, taste, and/or feel in that place. Ask each child to write and/or dictate at least two describing words that tell about their favorite place. Then have children explain their drawings to the class or to a partner.

© National Geographic Learning, a part of Cengage Learning, Inc.
For use with TE p. T78   **PM3.19**   Unit 3 | Visit the Farm!

Name _____

Read Sentences

1. See this cat.

2. Tap this cat.

3. Look at this can.

4. Tap this can.

5. See this cap.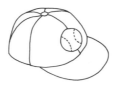

6. Tap this mat.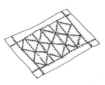

Directions: Discuss the pictures. Have partners read the sentences together and perform the actions.

For use with TE p. T81   **PM3.20**   **Unit 3** | Visit the Farm!

Name _____

Compare Stories

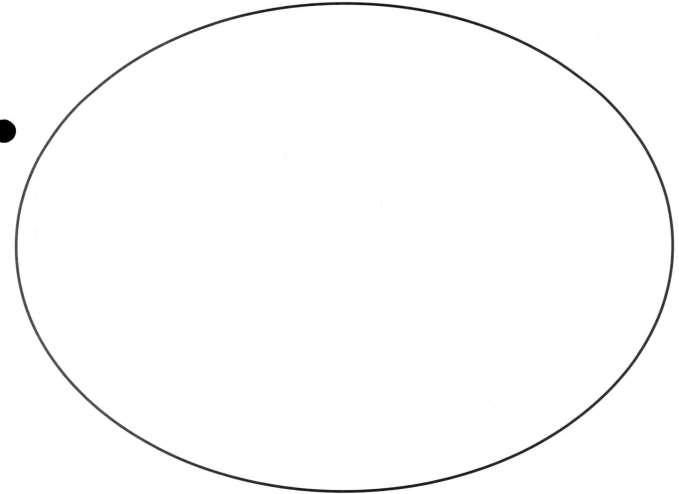

Directions: After discussing ways *The Tale of the Three Little Pigs* and *Honza's Little House* are alike, have children choose one idea to write and/or draw in the oval.

Phonics

Sound for <u>h</u>

1.

2.

3.

4.

5.

6.

7.

8.

9.

Directions: Name each picture with children. Have children color the pictures whose names begin with *h*.

© National Geographic Learning, a part of Cengage Learning, Inc.

For use with TE p. T100   **PM3.22**   **Unit 3** | Visit the Farm!

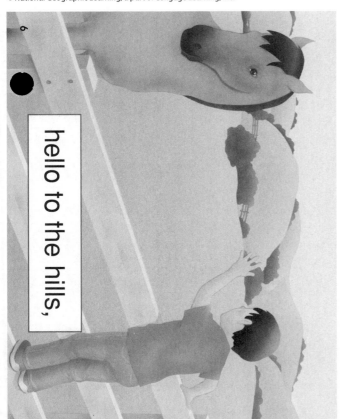

hello to the hills,

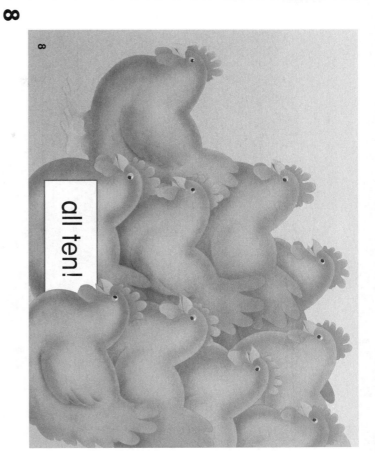

all ten!

hills

hen

Hh

Alphachant

Hh

by Lada Kratky
illustrated by Jean Hirashima

HAMPTON-BROWN

Hh

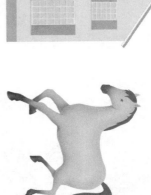

house

horse

Let's Chant!

Say hello to the house,

hello to the horse,

and hello to the hens,

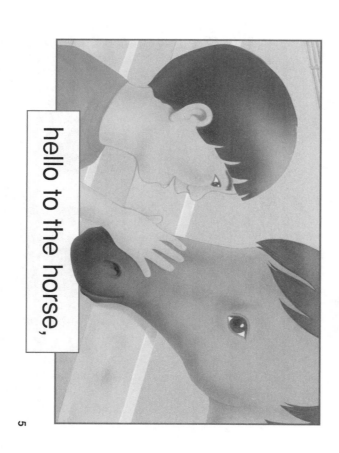

Phonics and High-Frequency Words

Letter and Word Cards

| High Frequency |
| **Word** |
| is |

✂

.	.	look	I	is
is	this	is	is
This	see	is	is
a	See	is	is

My Book of H h

Hh

Name _____

Complete Sentences

High Frequency
Word

is

---

1. This is a

_____ .

2. Is this a

_____ .

3. Look at the

_____ .

4. This is a

_____ .

Directions: Discuss the pictures and name each animal. Have partners take turns completing each sentence orally.

For use with TE p. T109   **PM3.26**   **Unit 3** | Visit the Farm!

Phonics

Blend Words with <u>h</u>

1. hat

2. mat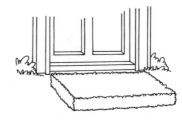

3. ham

4. cat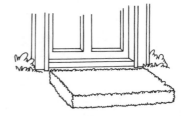

5. pan

Directions: Have children read each word and circle the picture that matches the word.

Name _____

Antonyms

 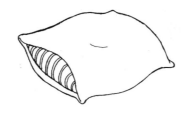 

Directions: Help children identify the pictures in each row. Then have them color the pictures that are opposites.

For use with TE p. T116   **PM3.28**   **Unit 3** | Visit the Farm!

Phonics and High Frequency Words

Read Sentences

1. I see this hat.

2. This hat is for me!

3. Look at this hat.

4. This hat is for Nan!

Directions: Discuss the pictures. Have partners read the sentences together.

© National Geographic Learning, a part of Cengage Learning, Inc.
For use with TE p. T119   **PM3.29**   Unit 3 | Visit the Farm!

Name _____

Compare Texts

Directions: After comparing *Baby Names* and "Baby Animals," have children draw and write about one way the selections are alike.

© National Geographic Learning, a part of Cengage Learning, Inc.
For use with TE p. T123   **PM3.30**   **Unit 3** | Visit the Farm!

Phonics

Sound for r

1.

2.

3.

4.

5.

6.

7.

8.

9.

Directions: Name each picture with children. Have children color the pictures whose names begin with the sound for the letter *r*.

For use with TE p. T138   **PM3.31**   **Unit 3** | Visit the Farm!

6

rain on the rabbit,

rabbit

rose

3

8

rain on my nose!

Alphachant

Rr

by Lada Kratky
illustrated by Gerardo Suzón

HAMPTON-BROWN

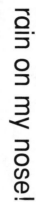

Rr

1

Rr

rain

roof

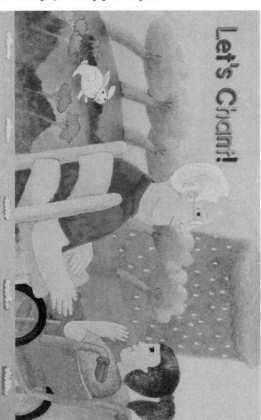

Let's Chant!

I like rain.

rain on the rose,

Rain on the roof,

Phonics and High-Frequency Words

Letter and Word Cards

High Frequency Word
like

.	.	like	like
like	this	like	like
a	is	like	like
Look	This	like	like

Directions: Duplicate and cut out the word and period cards. Each child will need one of each card for use during practice activities.

PM3.33

My Book of R r

R r

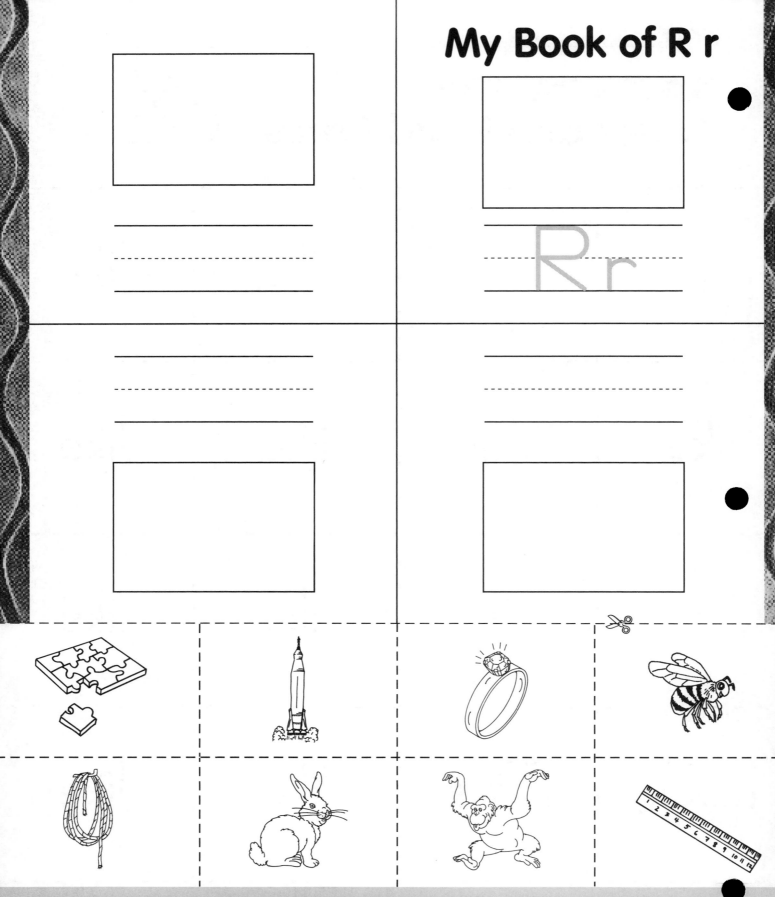

Directions: Have children trace the letter forms with a finger as you model letter formation. Then have children name and cut out the cards. Have them group the cards that start with the sound for *r* and paste one card on each page. Children can write *Rr* to label their pictures.

© National Geographic Learning, a part of Cengage Learning, Inc.
For use with TE p. T148   **PM3.34**   **Unit 3** | Visit the Farm!

High Frequency Words

Complete Sentences

High Frequency
Word

like

1. Look at this _____.

2. This _____ is like
   this _____.

3. Look at this _____.

4. Is this _____ like
   this _____?

Unit 3 | Visit the Farm!

Name _____

Compare Animals

Directions: Have children write the names of two animals they read about. Talk with them about ways in which the two animals are alike. Then have them draw one idea in the box.

© National Geographic Learning, a part of Cengage Learning, Inc.
For use with TE p. T150   **PM3.36**   **Unit 3** | Visit the Farm!

Blend Words with <u>r</u>

1. ram

2. pan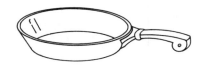

3. rat

4. man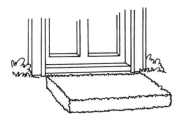

5. ran

Directions: Have children read each word and circle the picture that matches the word.

© National Geographic Learning, a part of Cengage Learning, Inc.
For use with TE p. T152   **PM3.37**   **Unit 3** | Visit the Farm!

Antonyms

<table>
<tr><td></td><td></td></tr>
<tr><td>_____
- - - - - - - - - - - - - - -
_____</td><td>_____
- - - - - - - - - - - - - - -
_____</td></tr>
</table>

Directions: Help children contrast two animals using antonyms. Then have children draw pictures of the animals to show their opposite meanings. Children can label their pictures with the antonyms.

© National Geographic Learning, a part of Cengage Learning, Inc.

For use with TE p. T156   **PM3.38**   **Unit 3** | Visit the Farm!

Phonics and High Frequency Words

Read Sentences

1. A ram can look like this.	**2.** A rat can look like this.
3. The ram ran like this.	**4.** The rat ran like this.

Directions: Have children read each sentence and draw a picture to match. Have partners take turns reading the sentences and showing their pictures.

Name _____

Compare Texts

Directions: After comparing *A World of Animals* and "A House for Me," have children draw and write about one way the selections are alike.

© National Geographic Learning, a part of Cengage Learning, Inc.
For use with TE p. T163   **PM3.40**   **Unit 3** | Visit the Farm!

Phonics

Sound for Ii

Directions: Name the letter and each picture with children. Have children cut out the cards. Ask partners to sort by middle sound, grouping the pictures with the middle sound for *i* with the *Ii* card. Have partners name all of the pictures in the *Ii* group.

© National Geographic Learning, a part of Cengage Learning, Inc.
For use with TE p. T192   **PM4.1**   **Unit 4** | All Kinds of Plants

Is an insect an inch?

An inch is an inch!

insect iguana

by Lada Kratky
photographed by Clem Spalding

HAMPTON-BROWN

Alphachant

Ii

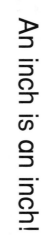

Ii

Ii

inch   inchworm

Let's Chant!

An inch is an inch.

Is an iguana an inch?

Is an inchworm an inch?

Name _____

Word Cards

| High Frequency |
| **Word** |
| and |

●

---

the	This	this	and
Hap	I	is	and ●
.	.	look	like	and
?	?	see	a	and

Directions: Duplicate and cut out the word cards and punctuation cards for use during practice activities.

PM4.3

Unit 4 | All Kinds of Plants

●

My Book of Ii

Ii

Directions: Have children trace the letter forms with a finger as you model letter formation. Then have children name and cut out the cards. Have them group the cards that start with the sound for *i* and paste one card on each page. Children can write *Ii* to label their pictures.

© National Geographic Learning, a part of Cengage Learning, Inc.
For use with TE p. T202

PM4.4

Unit 4 | All Kinds of Plants

Name _____

Read Sentences

1. Look at this.

2. I see this and this.

3. Look at this and this.

4. I like this. Mmm!

Directions: Discuss the pictures. Have partners read the sentences together.

For use with TE p. T203 **PM4.5** Unit 4 | All Kinds of Plants

Name _____

Cause and Effect

Cause	Effect

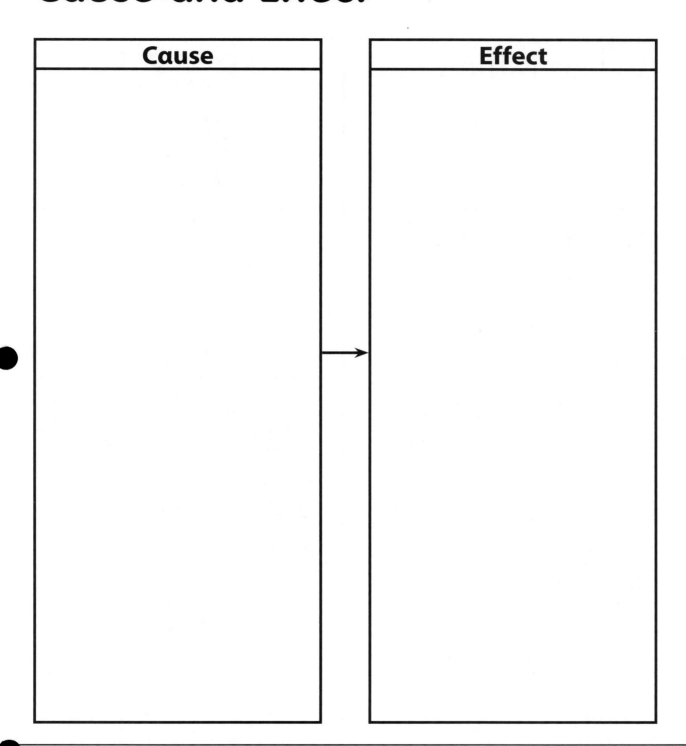

Directions: Have children think of something that happens in the story *Sofía and the Sunflower*. Ask them to draw what happens (the effect) in the right-hand box and why it happens (the cause) in the left-hand box. Encourage children to label their drawings.

© National Geographic Learning, a part of Cengage Learning, Inc.
For use with TE p. T204

PM4.6

Unit 4 | All Kinds of Plants

Name _____

Blend Words with i

1. This is Tim.	
2. Tim can sit.	
3. This is Sam.	
4. Can Sam sit in it?	

Directions: Have children read the sentences. Then have them label the characters Tim and Sam.

Name _____

Verbs

Directions: Have children use action words (verbs) in sentences to tell a partner what each person in the illustration is doing. Then have them add the labels *water, pick, put, dig,* and *plant* to the picture as they are able.

© National Geographic Learning, a part of Cengage Learning, Inc.
For use with TE p. T210   **PM4.8**   **Unit 4** | All Kinds of Plants

Read Sentences

1. See Min sit and look.

2. Min can see this.

3. Min can see this and this.

4. Hap and Pam and Tim see Min.

Directions: Discuss the pictures. Have partners read the sentences together.

Name _____

Compare Fairy Tales

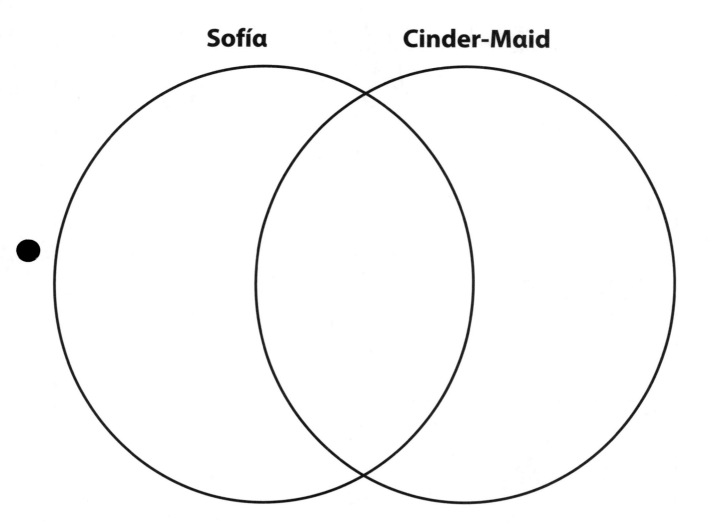

Sofía   **Cinder-Maid**

Directions: Have children use pictures and words to tell how the fairy tales *Sofía and the Sunflower* and *Cinder-Maid and the Oak Tree* are alike and different. Children can draw on a separate piece of paper as needed.

Unit 4 | All Kinds of Plants

PM4.11

Phonics

Sound for f_

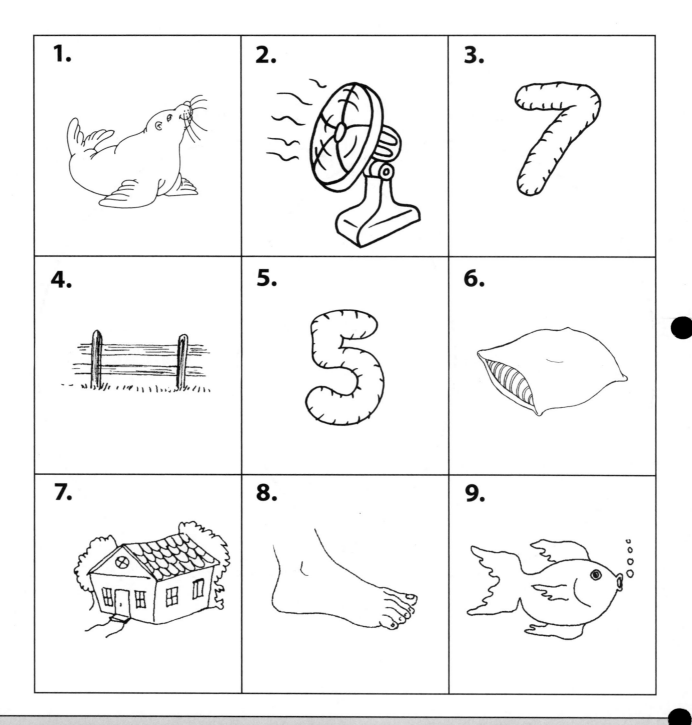

1.	**2.**	**3.**
4.	**5.**	**6.**
7.	**8.**	**9.**

Directions: Name each picture with children. Have children color the pictures whose names begin with *f*.

PM4.11

Unit 4 | All Kinds of Plants

under the fence,

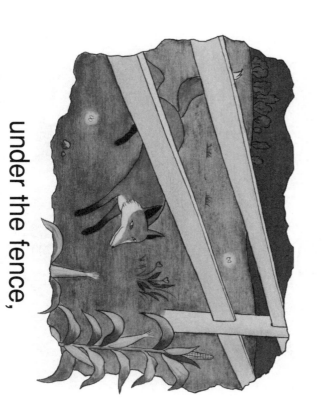

into your den. Home again.

by Lada Kratky
illustrated by Stefano Vitale

HAMPTON-BROWN

Alphachant

Ff

fence

farm

Ff

Ff

fox

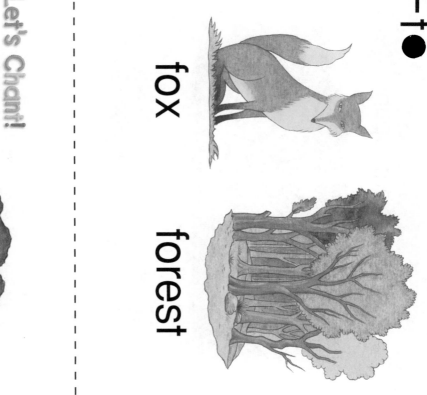

forest

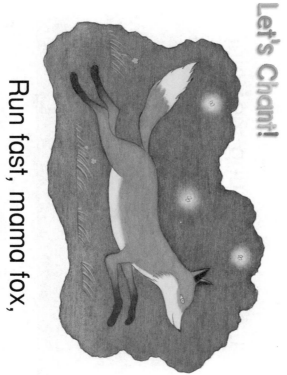

Let's Chant!

Run fast, mama fox,

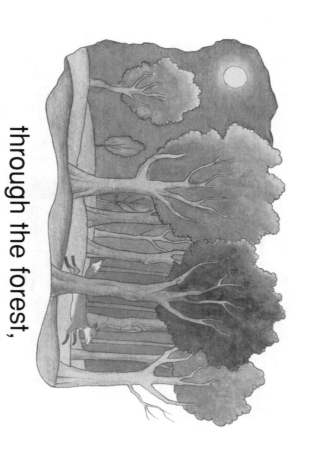

past the farm,

through the forest,

High Frequency Words

Word Cards

look	is	for	for
my	like	This	for
Look	and	a	for
. .	I	for	for

PM4.13

My Book of Ff

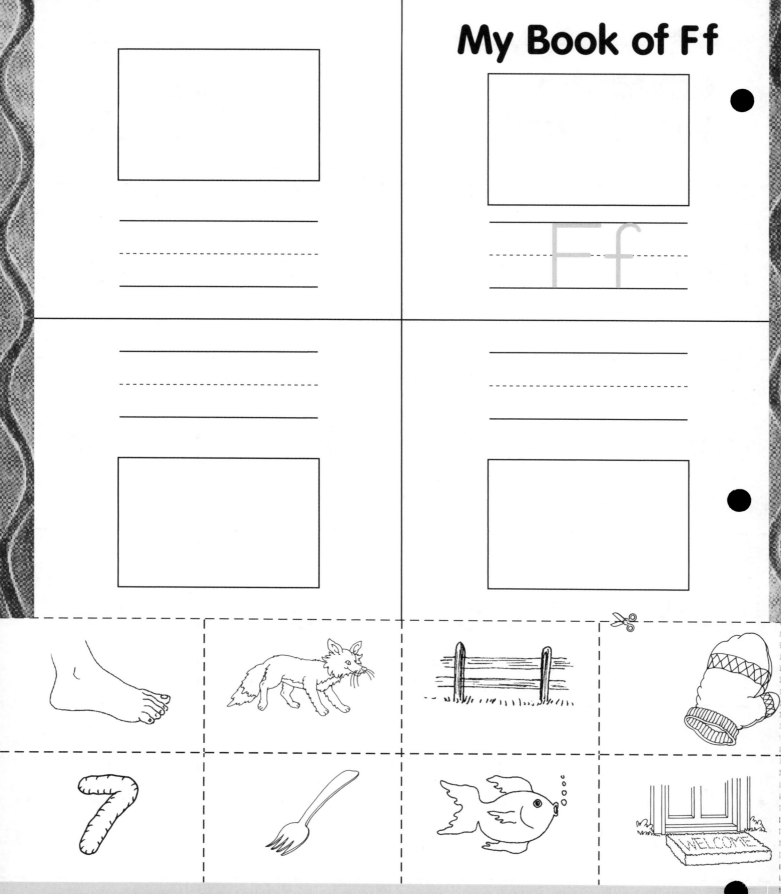

Ff

Directions: Have children trace the letter forms with a finger as you model letter formation. Then have children name and cut out the cards. Have them group the cards that start with the sound for *f* and paste one card on each page. Children can write *Ff* to label their pictures.

High Frequency Words

Read Sentences

1. This is for a rat.	**2.** This hat is for a man.
3. This mat is for a cat.	**4.** This pin is for a rip.

Directions: Have children read each sentence and draw a picture to match. Have partners read the sentences and share their pictures.

© National Geographic Learning, a part of Cengage Learning, Inc.
For use with TE p. T243

PM4.15

Unit 4 | All Kinds of Plants

Sequence

Directions: Have children draw a picture of what happens last in *Just One Seed*. Then help them write a sentence to tell about the event.

For use with TE p. T244   **PM4.16**   **Unit 4** | All Kinds of Plants

Phonics

Blend Words with f

1. This is a fan.

2. Is this cat fat?

3. This can fit
   a man.

4. This has a fin.

Directions: Have children read each sentence and draw a line to the picture it matches.

© National Geographic Learning, a part of Cengage Learning, Inc.
For use with TE p. T246

PM4.17

Unit 4 | All Kinds of Plants

Name _____

Directions: Have children color the page. Then have a partner act out an action they see or other actions that might happen in the garden. The other partner should then guess the action. Have partners add a new character to the picture for each new action they name.

For use with TE p. T250   **PM4.18**   **Unit 4** | All Kinds of Plants

Name _____

Read Sentences

1. This is Sam and Fan.

2. This is for Fan!

3. Fan can fit this in.

4. Sam and I fit this in.

Directions: Discuss the pictures. Have partners read the sentences.

Name _____

Compare Sequences

_____

- -

_____

_____

- -

_____

Directions: After discussing what happened in _The Little Red Hen_ and _Just One Seed,_ have children draw and write about what happened first, next, and last in one of the stories.

© National Geographic Learning, a part of Cengage Learning, Inc.
For use with TE p. T257 **PM4.20** **Unit 4** | All Kinds of Plants

Phonics

Sound for g

Directions: Name the letter and each picture with children. Have children cut out the cards. Ask partners to sort by beginning sound, grouping the pictures with the beginning sound for *g* with the *Gg* card. Then, have partners name all of the pictures in the *Gg* group.

For use with TE p. T272   **PM4.21**   **Unit 4** | All Kinds of Plants

6

The goose goes in the gate.

8

but he's too late!

goose

gorilla

Gg

3

Alphachant™

Gg

by Lada Kratky
illustrated by Peter Grosshauser

HAMPTON-BROWN

1

Gg

gate

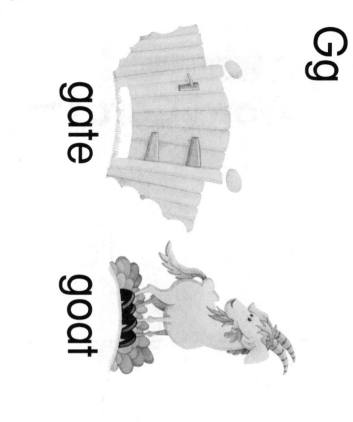

goat

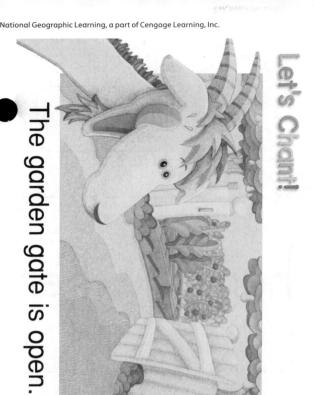

The garden gate is open.

The goat goes in the gate.

The gorilla goes in the gate,

High Frequency Words

Word Cards

●

I	for	here	here
! !	Here	a	here
, ,	is	like	here
. .	a	and	here

My Book of G g

G g

Directions: Have children trace the letter forms with a finger as you model letter formation. Then have children name and cut out the cards. Have them group the cards that start with the sound for *g* and paste one card on each page. Children can write *Gg* to label their pictures.

© National Geographic Learning, a part of Cengage Learning, Inc.

For use with TE p. T280

PM4.24

Unit 4 | All Kinds of Plants

Name _____

Read Sentences

1. I look in here for him.

2. I can fit this in here.

3. I sit here.

4. I nap here. I like it!

Directions: Discuss the pictures. Have partners read the sentences together.

Name _____

Sequence

First:

↓

Next:

↓

Last:

Directions: Have children draw steps to tell what to do *first, next,* and *last* to make an apple pie. Then have them discuss the steps. Children's sequences will vary.

© National Geographic Learning, a part of Cengage Learning, Inc.
For use with TE p. T282   **PM4.26**

Blend Words with g

1. Gas is in this.

---

2. It can fit in the gap.

---

3. Gas is in here.

---

4. Can this fit in the gap?

Directions: Review the meaning of *gap:* "a hole in something." Have children read each sentence. Discuss the pictures.

Name _____

Grammar

Verbs

_____
- -
_____

Directions: Have children draw a picture of themselves doing an action. Then have them write an action word (verb) to tell about what they are doing.

© National Geographic Learning, a part of Cengage Learning, Inc.
For use with TE p. T288

PM4.28

Unit 4 | All Kinds of Plants

Phonics and High Frequency Words

Read Sentences

High Frequency
Word

here

1. Is it in here?

2. Fit this in the gap.

3. Is gas in this?

4. I like it here!

Directions: Have partners read the sentences. Discuss the pictures.

Comprehension

Sequence

First:

↓

Next:

↓

Last:

Directions: Have children draw three steps to make something of their choice, as in the selections *How to Grow a Garden* and *Apples*.

© National Geographic Learning, a part of Cengage Learning, Inc.
For use with TE p. T295   **PM4.30**   **Unit 4** | All Kinds of Plants

Name _____

Sound for <u>b</u>

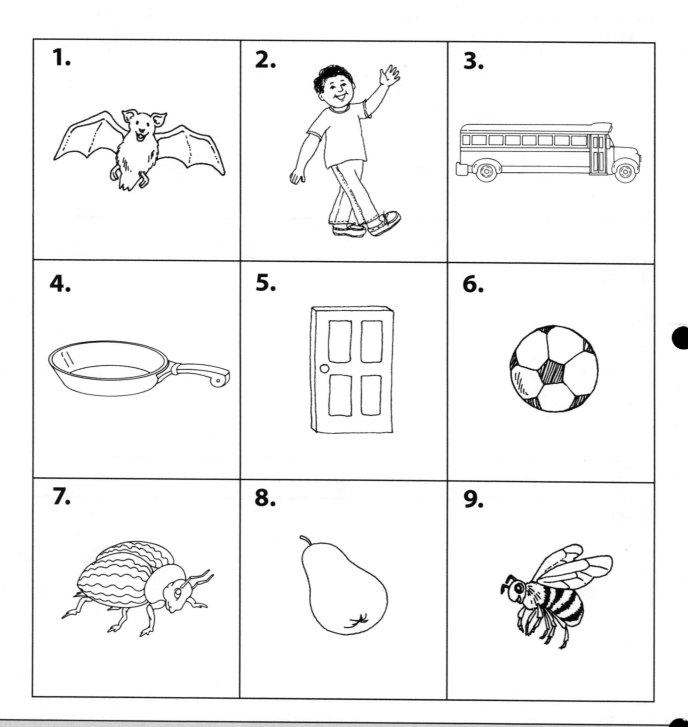

1.

2.

3.

4.

5.

6.

7.

8.

9.

Directions: Name each picture with children. Have children color the pictures whose names begin with *b*.

a bow on a bear,

What a fuss!

bear

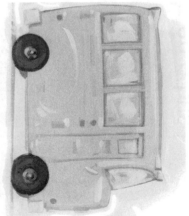

bus

Bb

Alphachant

Bb

by Lada Kratky
illustrated by Lori Lohstoeter

HAMPTON-BROWN

Bb

bee

bow

Let's Chant!

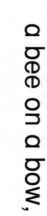

I see a bee,

a bee on a bow,

and a bear on a bus.

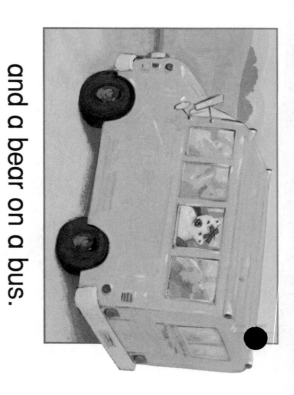

2

4

5

7

Name _____

High Frequency Words

Word Cards

High Frequency Word
go

this	a	and	go
See	I	for	go
. .	Is	here	go
? ?	see	a	go

Directions: Duplicate and cut out the word cards for use during practice activities.

For use with TE pp. T312, T313, T321   **PM4.33**   **Unit 4** | All Kinds of Plants

My Book of Bb

B b

Directions: Have children trace the letter forms with a finger as you model letter formation. Then have children name and cut out the cards. Have them group the cards that start with the sound for *b* and paste one card on each page. Children can write *Bb* to label their pictures.

© National Geographic Learning, a part of Cengage Learning, Inc.

For use with TE p. T320

PM4.34

Unit 4 | All Kinds of Plants

Name _____

Read Sentences

1. I go in here.

2. Can I go in here?

3. See him go!

4. Can I go in here?

5. I go and go!

Directions: Discuss the pictures. Have partners read the sentences together.

For use with TE p. T321   **PM4.35**   **Unit 4** | All Kinds of Plants

Name _____

Main Idea and Details

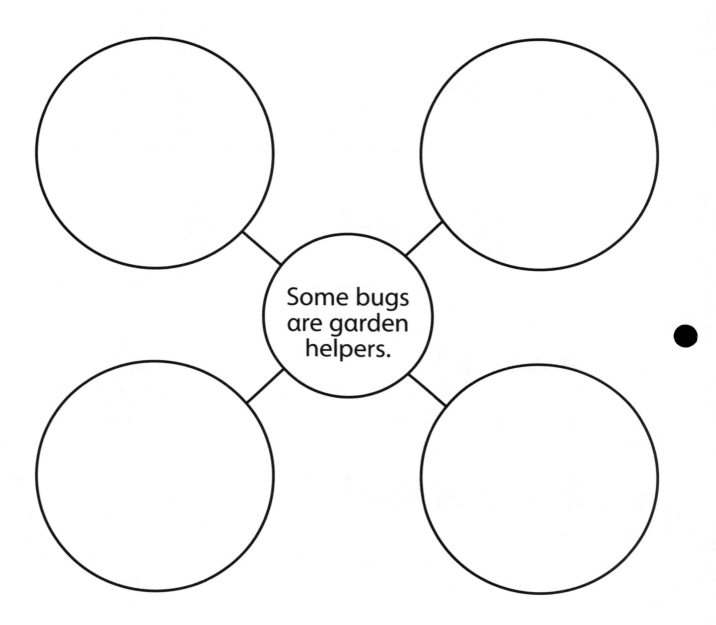

Some bugs are garden helpers.

Directions: Discuss the main idea of *Garden Helpers* with children. Read aloud the text in the center circle of the graphic organizer. Then have children draw or write four supporting details from the essay in the outer circles.

For use with TE p. T322 **PM4.36** **Unit 4** | All Kinds of Plants

Phonics

Blend Words with <u>b</u>

1. It is big.

2. This is a bat.

3. I see a bib.

4. I see a bag.

Directions: Have children read each sentence and draw a line to the picture it matches.

Name _____

Verbs

boy **read**	**brush** **teeth**
sing **dad**	**ducks** **swim**
fly **high**	**fun** **dance**

Directions: Discuss each picture with children. Read aloud the two words below each picture. Have children circle the word that tells about the action in the picture.

For use with TE p. T328   **PM4.38**   Unit 4 | All Kinds of Plants

Name _____

Read Sentences

1. I am big.
I can go in here.

2. I go here.
I bit this.

3. See Kim.
Kim bit it.

4. Mom and I can
go here.

Directions: Discuss the pictures. Have partners read the sentences.

Name _____

Compare Details

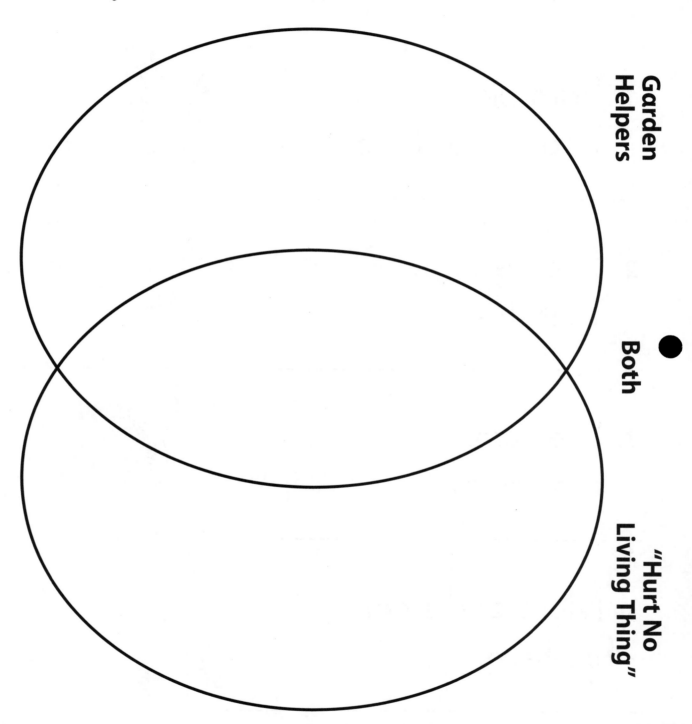

Garden Helpers

Both

"Hurt No Living Thing"

Directions: Have children draw and write details from the Big Book *Garden Helpers* and the poem "Hurt No Living Thing" to show how the two selections are the same and different.

For use with TE p. T335   **PM4.40**   **Unit 4** | All Kinds of Plants